70 YEARS OF POPULAR MUSIC

THE THIRTIES

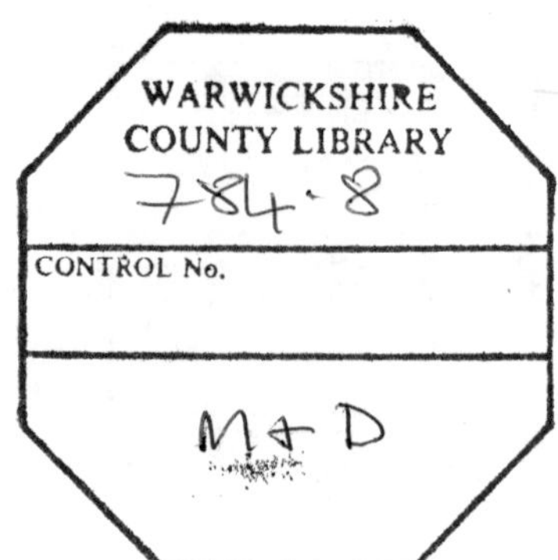

IMP
First published 1985

Exclusive Distributors: International Music Publications, Southend Road, Woodford Green, Essex IG8 8HN, England
215-2-271, Order ref: 09907, ISBN 0.86359.243.0

Cover design by Howard Brown/Peter Wood. Photography by Peter Wood

ALL THE THINGS YOU ARE

Words by OSCAR HAMMERSTEIN II
Music by JEROME KERN

found my ad - ven - ture, Touch-ing your hand, my heart beats the fast - er,
B7susp. E
B7
All that I want in all of this world is you.
G
Am7
D7
G
C7
REFRAIN
p cantabile
You are the prom-ised kiss of spring-time That
p cantabile
Fm7
Bbm
Eb9
Cm
Eb7
Abmaj7
makes the lone - ly win - ter seem long
Dbmaj7
Bbm
Fm
G7
C maj7
C6

You are the breath-less hush of eve-ning That
Cm7
Fm7
B♭9
Gm B♭7
E♭maj7
trem-bles on the brink of a love-ly song. You are the
A♭maj7
Fm Cm
D7
G
G maj7
G6
G
G maj7
an - gel glow that lights a star, The dear-est
Am7
D7♭9
C
D9
G
rall.
things I know are what you are.
rall.
Am6
(susp. B♮)
Am6
B♭
B
B7♭9
E
A♭+

p a tempo
Some day my hap-py arms will hold you, And
p a tempo
Fm7 Bbm7 Eb9 Cm Eb7 Abmaj7
mf ten.
some day I'll know that mo-ment di - vine, When
mf
Db Dbmaj7 Bbm7(b5) Ab Abdim
Lento
1
all the things you are, are mine!
Bbm7 Eb9 Ab Bbm6 C7
2
a tempo
mine!
a tempo
R.H.
p
pp
Ab

ANYTHING GOES

Words and Music
by COLE PORTER

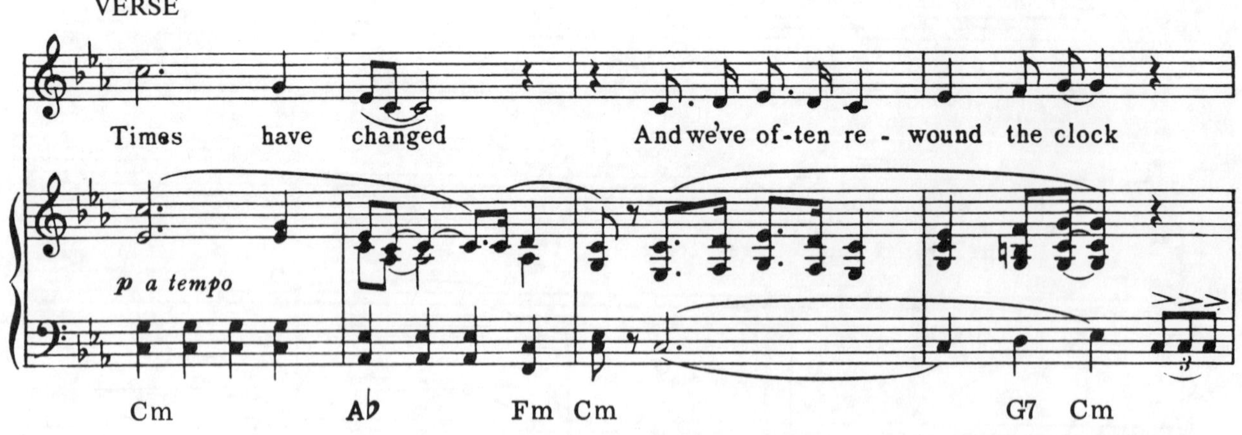

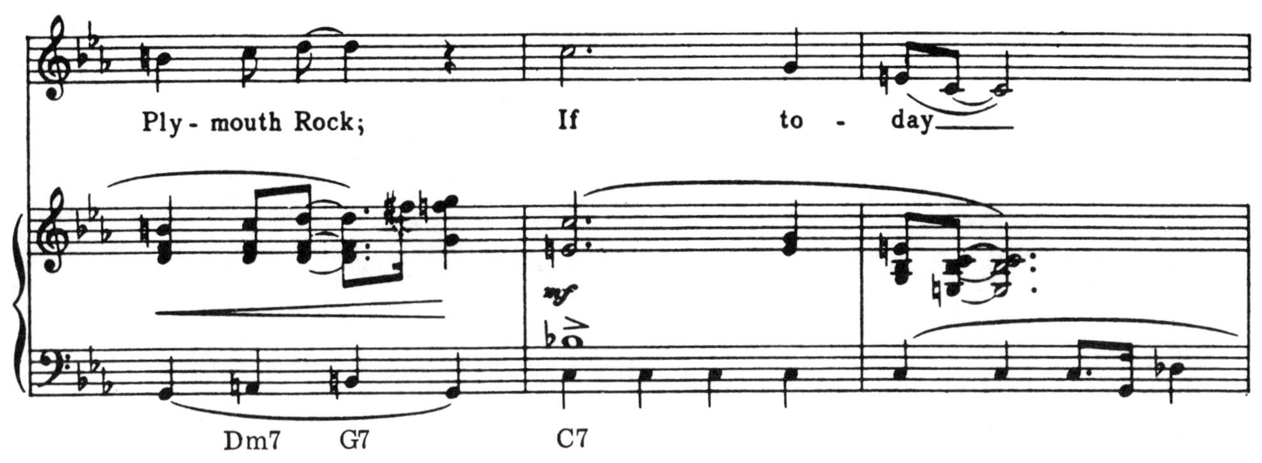
Ply - mouth Rock; If to - day
mf
Dm7 G7 C7

A - ny shock they should try to stem, 'Stead of land - ing on
C7 Fm C7 Fm G7

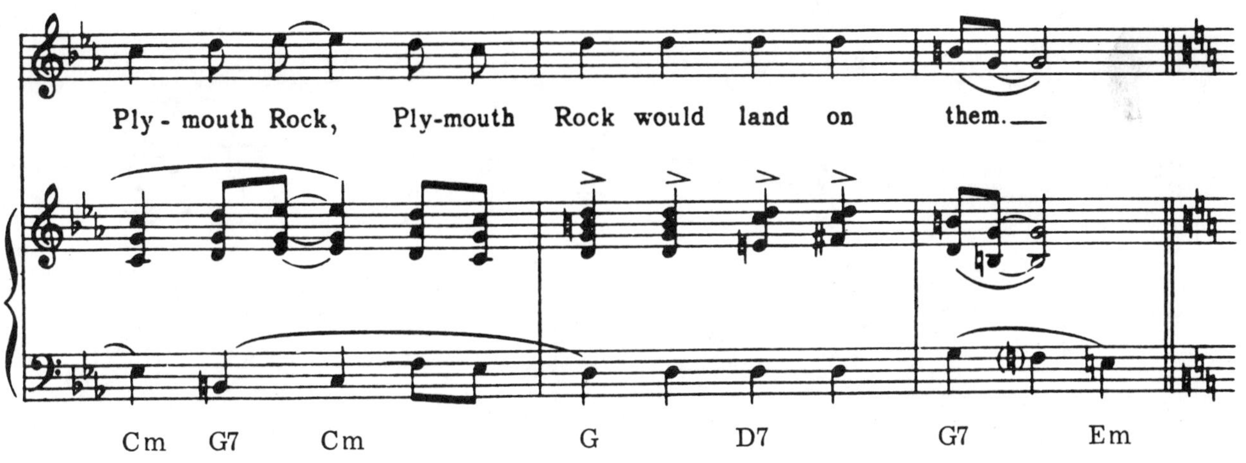
Ply - mouth Rock, Ply-mouth Rock would land on them.
Cm G7 Cm G D7 G7 Em

REFRAIN
In old - en days a glimpse of stock - ing Was look'd on as some-thing shock - ing, Now heav-en knows, A - ny-thing goes. Good auth - ors too who once knew bet - ter words Now on - ly use four-let - ter words, writ-ing prose, A - ny-thing goes. The world has gone mad to-day And good's
p-mf
mf
G7 C Am C Am
C7 Dm7 C Dm7 Dm7-5 C Dm C G+
C Am C Am C7
Dm7 C Dm7 Dm7-5 C Dm C B7 E

bad to-day, And black's white to-day, And day's night to-day, When most guys to-day That women
B9 B7 Em B7 Em
prize to-day, Are just sil-ly gig-ol-os;
So though I'm not a
Em7 C#0 D#0 C#0 G7 C
great ro-manc-er I know that {you're / I'm} bound to an-swer when {I / you} pro-pose,
Am C Am C7 Dm7 C
A-ny-thing goes.
1
mf
In
2
goes.
sf
Dm7 C Dm7 C Dm7 C F#0 G7 C Dm7 C Dm7 C

ALL OF ME

SEE P.12 FOR
INTRODUCTION AND VERSE

Words and Music by
SEYMOUR SIMONS and GERALD MARKS

REFRAIN Moderato

them, Your good-bye left me with eyes that cry,
G7 C E7
How can I go on dear with-out you. You took the
A7 Dm F6
part that once was my heart, So why not take all of
Fm6 C7♮ Gm6 A9 A7 Fm6 G7
1
me.
C B7(9♮) Cdim Dm7 G7+
2
me.
C Fm C
FINE

INTRODUCTION AND VERSE

I'LL STRING ALONG WITH YOU

Words by AL DUBIN
Music by HARRY WARREN

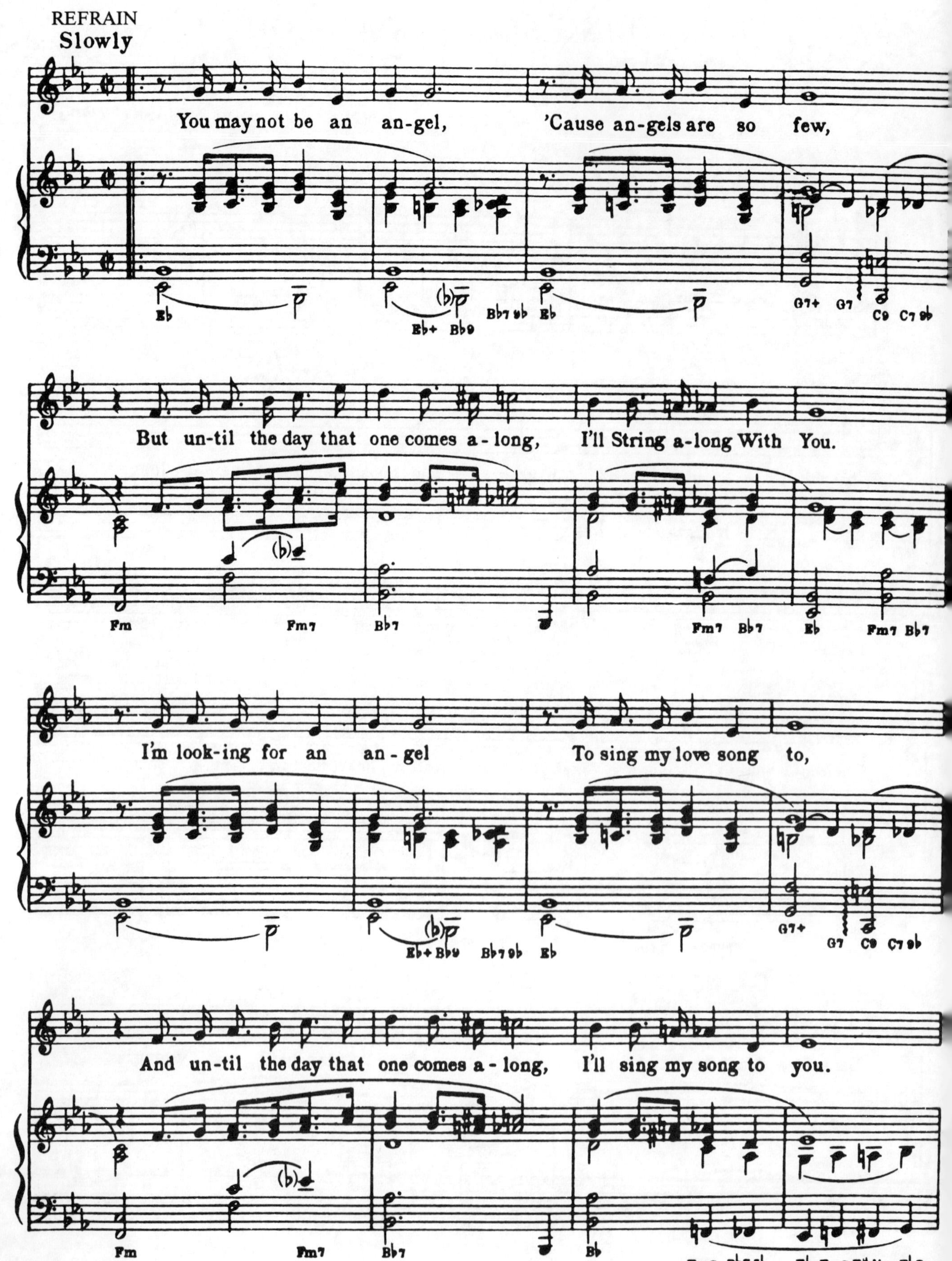
REFRAIN
Slowly
You may not be an an-gel, 'Cause an-gels are so few,
But un-til the day that one comes a-long, I'll String a-long With You.
I'm look-ing for an an-gel To sing my love song to,
And un-til the day that one comes a-long, I'll sing my song to you.

For ev-'ry lit-tle fault that you have, Say! I've got three or four,
R.H.
Ab
Abm
Eb
Gbdim
Bb9
Edim
Fm7
F#dim D7
The hu-man lit-tle faults you do have, Just make me love you more,
You may not be an
Eb
Ebmaj7 Eb7
Eb
Abm6
Eb
F9 Bb7+
Bb9+(9b)
Eb
an-gel,
But still I'm sure you'll do,
So un-til the day that
Eb+ Bb9 Bb7 9b
Eb
G7+ G7
C9 C7 9b
Fm
Fm7
1
2
one comes a-long
I'll String a-long With You.
You.
pp
Bb7
Bb13
Fm7 Bb7 5b
Eb
B9
Fm7 Bb13
Eb
Db9
Eb

BYE BYE BLUES

Words and Music by FRED HAMM, DAVE BENNETT,
BERT LOWN and CHAUNCEY GRAY

REFRAIN *2nd time f*

EMBRACEABLE YOU

Words by IRA GERSHWIN
Music by GEORGE GERSHWIN

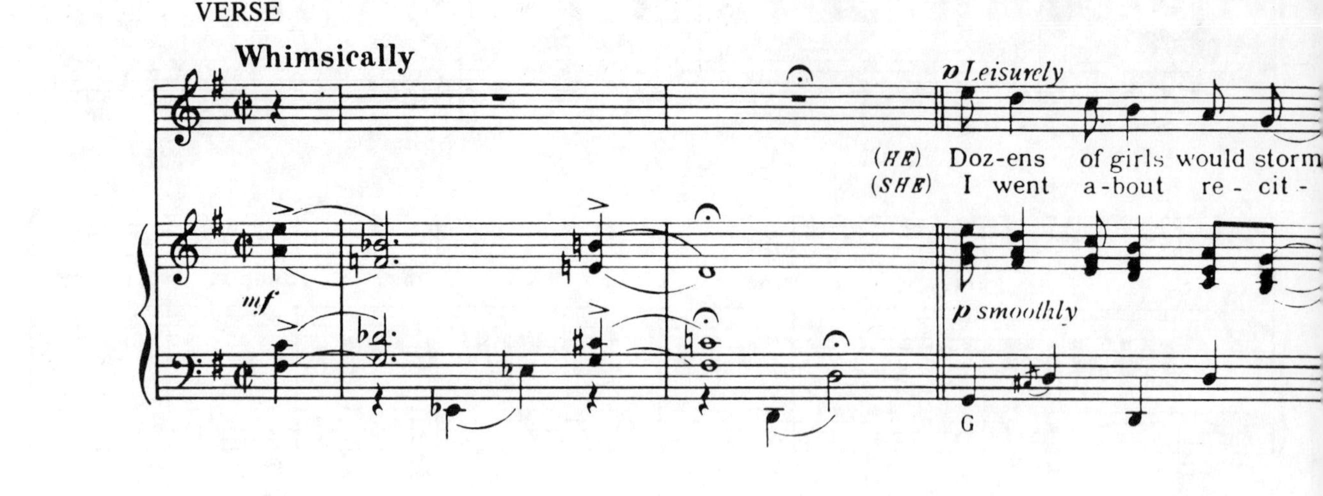

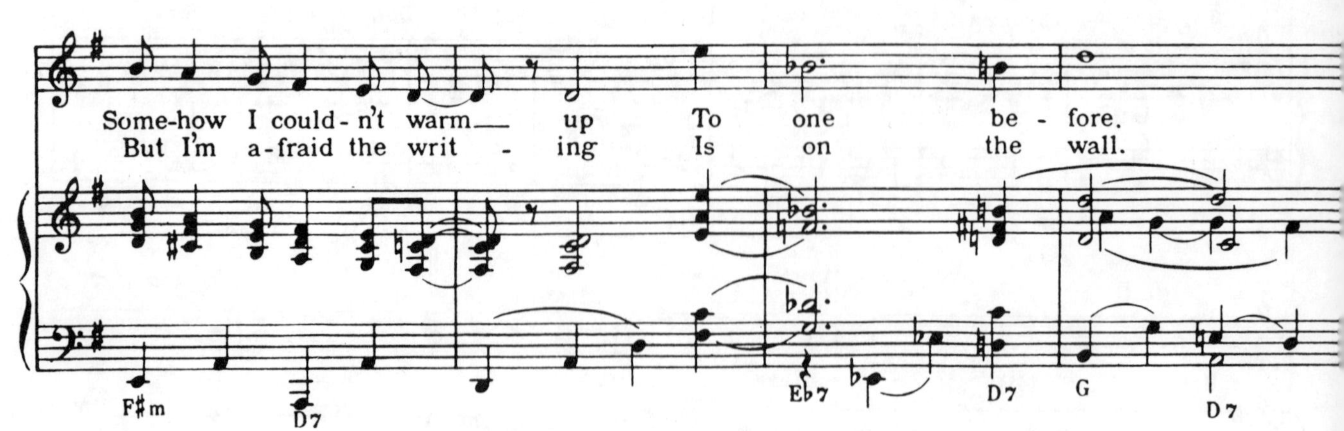

What was it that con-trolled me? What kept my love-life
My nose I used to turn up When you'd be-siege my
G
F♯7
lean? My in - tu - i - tion told me You'd come
heart; Now I com-plete - ly burn up When you're
B
F♯7
B
on the scene. La-dy, lis-ten to the rhy-thm of my
slow to start. I'm a - fraid you'll have to take the con-se -
Am7
open
D7
G
Em
Em
add C♯
Em
Em
add C♯
rall. e dim.
heart - beat, And you'll get just what I mean.
-quenc - es; You've up - set the ap - ple cart.
rall. e dim.
Em
Em
add C♯
Em
A7
Am
D
Am
D
Am
D
Am
D7

REFRAIN (*Rhythmically*)

I love all the man-y charms a-bout you;
But hang it! Come on, let's glo - ri-fy love!
G C♯dim D7 C Ddim D7
A-bove all I want my arms a-bout you.
Ding dang it! You'll shout, "En - core!" if I love.
Don't be a
Don't be a
A F7 D7 G7 G7 with C C♯dim G7 C
naugh-ty ba - by, Come to pa-pa, Come to pa-pa, do! My sweet em -
naugh-ty pa - pa, Come to ba-by, Come to ba-by, do! My sweet em -
L.H.
Am add F♯ D7 Em E♭ aug.5 G Em add C♯ G
1
2
-brace - a-ble you!
-brace - a-ble you!
Cm add A D7 G E♭ A D7 G

A FOGGY DAY

Words by IRA GERS
Music by GEORGE GERS

REFRAIN (brighter but warmly)
A fog-gy day in Lon-don town Had me low and
C7 F F♯m6 Gm7 C13 C13-9 F F7 Fm6
had me down. I viewed the morn-ing with a-larm, The Brit-ish Mu-se-um had
G13 G7+ C9 Fmaj7 (-5) C7+ F9 B♭maj7 B♭m6 Fmaj7 D9
lost its charm. How long, I won-dered, could this thing last? But the age of mir-a-cles
G13 G9+C9 C7 F F♯m6 Gm7sus Gm7 C13 C13-9 F F7 Fm6 Gm Fm6
had-n't passed, For, sud-den-ly, I saw you there And through fog-gy Lon-don town the sun was
G13 G7+ C9 F11 F13 F13-9 Gm9-5 Dm Gm7-5 F B♭ Fmaj7 B♭
B♭maj9
shin-ing ev-'ry-where. A where.
Gm7 G9 C11 C7 F C7 F7 B♭7 C7 F C7 F7 B♭7 Dm6 B♭6
Fmaj7 Gm7-5 Fmaj7 Gm7-5 Fmaj7

FOR YOU

Words by AL D
Music by JOE B

— For you. (Boy) I'll make_ a string of pearls_ out of the dew,
(Girl) I'll wear_ a string of pearls_ made of the dew.
G7 G9 C Am7 Dm7 G7 C Dm7
— For you, For you. O-ver the
G7 C° Dm7 G7 G9 C6 B7 Em
high-way and o-ver the street, Car-pets of clo-ver I'll lay at your
Am Em Am6 Em B7 Em C6 E♭7
feet, Oh, there's noth-ing in this world_ I would-n't do For you,
G7 G7+ C Dm7 G7 C° Dm7
1. 2.
— For you. you.
G7 (♭9) C6 C° Dm7 G7 C6 G7 C6

GOODY GOODY

Words and M
JOHNNY MERCER and MATTY MA

C Bb13 A7 Dm A7 Dm A7
et some-one and now_ you know how it feels, GOOD-Y - GOOD-Y! So you gave him your heart, too_ just as
m A7-9 Dm D7 Am7 D7 Dm7 G7 G7 C
I gave mine to you_ And he broke it in lit - tle piec-es, now how do you do._ So you lie a-wake just sing-
And he stuck it in his_ col - lec-tion, sec-tion nine-ty two_
G+ C6 C C7 G7+ C9 C7 G7+ C9 C+ F A7 Dm
- in' the blues all night, GOOD-Y - GOOD-Y! So you think that love's a bar - rel of dy-na-mite_ You
F Fm C/G G7+ C A7 Em7 A7
had it coming to ya, And you don't like it do ya? GOOD-Y - GOOD-Y for him GOOD-Y - GOOD-Y for me
1
2
n7 A7 D7 Dm7 G9+ G7-9 C Am7 Dm7 G7 C Dm7 G13 C
And I hope you're sat-is - fied you ras - cal you. So you you._

HOMETOWN

Words and M
JIMMY KENNEDY and MICHAEL

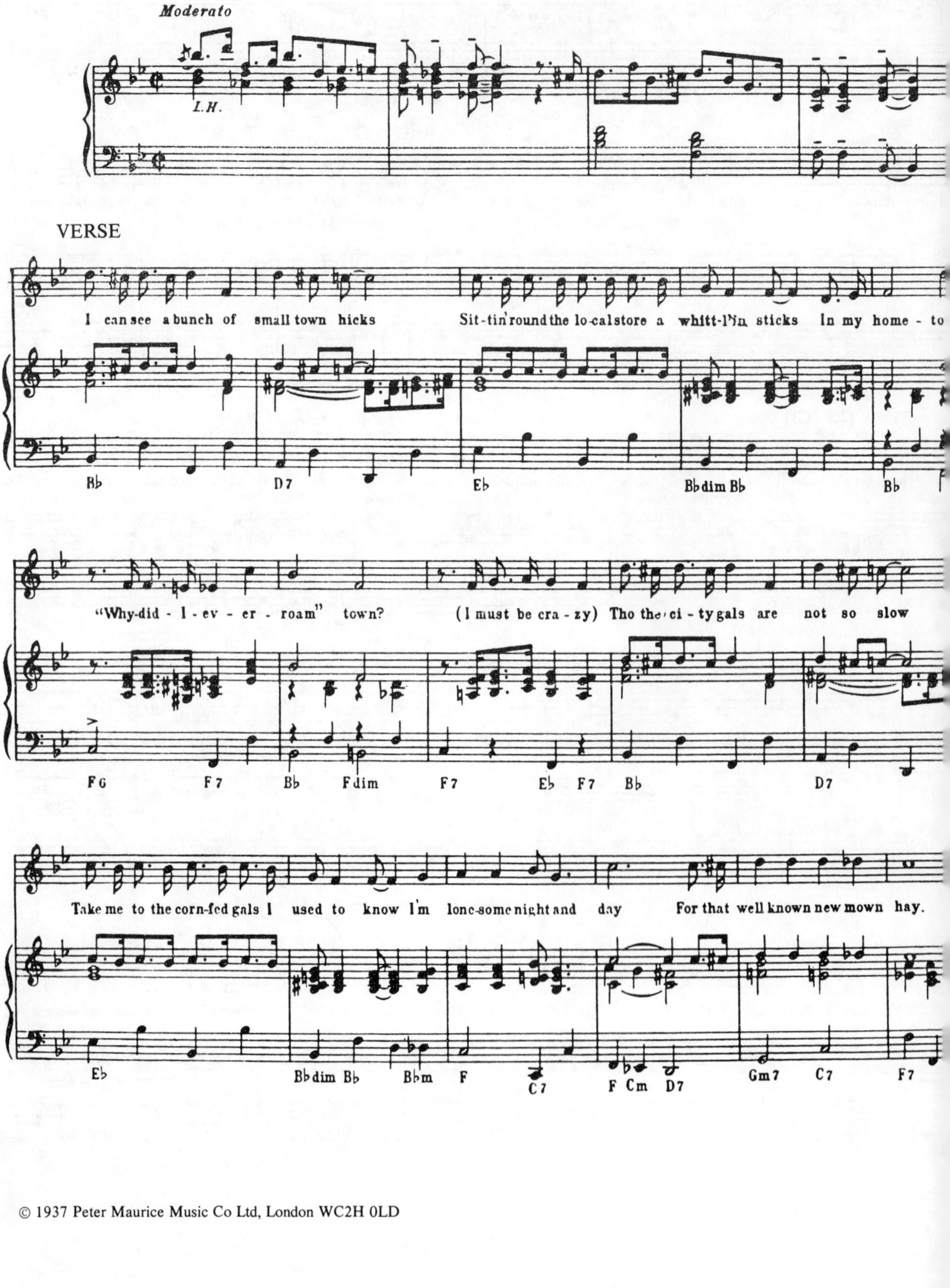

REFRAIN

Home - town want to wander round your back streets, See your tum-ble down old shack streets I'd love to
Bb D7 G7 C7 F7 Fdim F7 C7 F7
walk in on those corny country cousins of mine. Home - town where the dove's are softly coo - in', where there's always nothin'
Bb Gm F7 Gdim F7 Bb D7 G7 C7
do - in' I'd get a welcome from those corny country cousins of mine. There's an old school house door we used to tumble thro' at
F7 Fdim F7 C7 F7 Bb Gm Eb F7 Bb D7 C# D7 G7 F# G7
four And a small candy store where I could go a dozen lol lipops and come for more Home - town where the garden trees are
C7 B C7 F7 Eb Bb dim F7 Bb D7
sha - dy, Where our Eadie was a la - dy I'm going back to see those corny country cousins of mine. cousins of mine.
G7 C7 F7 Fdim F7 C7 F7 Bb Gm Eb F7 Bb Eb F7 Bb
1
2

I APOLOGISE

Words and Music by AL HOFFMA
AL GOODHART and ED NELSC

It's my fault All my fault, That we're a - part.
I loved you I still do, You must sur - mise,
G A7 D7 G
I'd give an - y - thing if I could be Back with you, sweet - heart.
That I need you more than ev - er, dear. Now I re - a - lize.
rit.
Bb Cm7 Cm7b5 F7 Fm7 Bb7
REFRAIN
If I told a lie, If I made you cry, When I said goodbye I'm sor - ry
Eb Fm7 Bb7 Gm C7 Fm G7
From the bottom of my heart, dear, I a - pol - o - gise.
Eb C dim Eb C7 Fm7 Gm Bb7 Eb
If I caused you pain, I know I'm to blame Must have been insane, Be- lieve me,
Eb Fm7 Bb7 Gm C7 Fm G7

From the bottom of my heart, dear, I a-pol-o-gise.
E♭
C dim
E♭
C7
Fm7
B♭7
E♭
I re-a-lize I've been un-fair to you, Please let me make a-mends.
Gm
A7
Cm6
D7
Gm
Don't say that you for-got the love we knew. Af-ter all, we were more than friends.
B♭
B♭m
Cm7
Cm7♭5
F7
F9
B♭7
Gm
B♭7
If I've made you blue, I've had heart-aches too. Now I beg of you for-give me,
E♭
Fm
B♭7
Gm
C7
Fm
G7
1.
2.
From the bottom of my heart, dear, I a-pol-o-gise. gise.
F♭
C♭dim
E♭
C7
Fm7
B♭7
E♭
Gdim
B♭9
B♭+7
E♭
B♭+7
E♭

I'M CONFESSIN' (THAT I LOVE YOU)

Words by AL J NEIBURG
Music by DOC DAUGHERTY and ELLIS REYNOLDS

REFRAIN

G
I'm con-fess-in' that I love you; Tell me, do you love me too?
G D+ G(7♯) G F♯7 D7 E9
I'm con-fess-in' that I need you, hon-est I do, need you ev-'ry mo-ment!
A7 D7 Am7 D7 G Am7 D7
In your eyes I read such strange things, But your lips de-ny they're true;
G D+ G(7♯) G F♯7 D7 E9
Will your an-swer real-ly change things, mak-ing me blue?
A7 D7 Am7 D7 G G Cm6 G D C D7

C
I'm a-fraid, some day, you'll leave me, say-ing "Can't we still be friends?"
G7 Dm7 G7 G9 G9+ C C6 C7 B7 B♭7
D
If you go, you know you'll grieve me, all in life on you de - pends,
G
A7 A9 Adim A9 Ddim D7 Am7 D7 Am7 D7
Am I guess-in' that you love me dream-ing dreams of you in vain? I'm con-fess-in' that I
G D+ G (7♯) G F♯7 D7 E9 A7
1
2
love you, o-ver a - gain. - gain.
D7 Am7 D7 G Am7 D7 G D9 G6
D.C.

I GOT RHYTHM

Words by IRA GERSHWI
Music by GEORGE GERSHWI

day - ful of song, Why should-n't we sing a -
Gmi add E
B♭7
Gmi
Gmi7
Cmi7
F7
- long?
I'm chip - per all the day,
sf
B♭
Fmi
B♭
Fmi
B♭
D
D7
Faug.5
D7
(♭)
Hap - py with my lot.
How do I get that way?
sf
Cmi7
E♭7
D
D7
Faug.5
D7
Look at what I've got:
f
Cmi7
F7
Edim.
G♭7
F7
B♭mi add G
Ddim
F7

REFRAIN (with abandon)
p - mf
I got rhy - thm, I got mu - sic,
Bb Gmi Cmi7 F7 Gmi 7 with C Edim Cmi7 F7
I got my man, Who could ask for an-y-thing more?
Bb Gmi Cmi7 F7 Eb mi add C Bb F7 Bb C#dim F7
I got dais - es In green pas - tures, I got
Bb Gmi Cmi7 F7 Gmi7 with C Edim Cmi7 F7 Bb Gmi
my man, Who could ask for an-y-thing more? Old Man
Cmi7 F7 Eb mi add C Bb F7 Bb D7 C

Trouble, I — don't mind him, — You — won't
Ddim D7 G Daug.5 Dmi G7 C7 Bb
find him — 'Round — my door. I — got
Cdim C9 C7 with Gb F7 C7 F7 Bb Gmi
star - light, I — got sweet dreams, I — got my man, Who could
Cmi7 F7 Gmi7 with C Edim. Cmi7 F7 Bb Gmi Cmi7 F7 Ebmi add C
ask for an-y-thing more, Who could ask for an-y-thing more? more?
1 2
sfz
8
Bb Fmi G7 C7 F7 Bb Ab Gb Db Bb

IT'S ONLY A PAPER MOON

Words by BILLY ROSE and E Y HARBURG
Music by HAROLD ARLEN

REFRAIN
p-f a tempo
Say, it's on-ly a pa-per moon, Sail-ing o-ver a card-board sea; But it would-n't be make-believe If you be-lieved in me.
p-f a tempo
G D0 D7 G Dm Am7 D7 G F# D7
Yes, it's on-ly a can-vas sky, Hang-ing o-ver a mus-lin tree; But it would-n't be make-believe If you be-lieved in me.
G D0 D7 G Dm Am7 D7 G
With-out your love it's a hon-ky-tonk pa-rade; With-out your love, it's a mel-o-dy played in a penny ar-cade.
cantabile
Am7 E♭ Em C Em7 D7 G Am7 E♭ Bm G Dm E7 A7 D+
pf
It's a Barnum and Bai-ley world, Just as pho-ny as it can be; But it would-n't be make-believe If you be-lieved in me.
pf
G D0 D7 G Dm Am7 D7 G Am7 D7 G
1
2
sf

I'VE GOT YOU UNDER MY SKIN

Words and Music
by COLE PORTER

Fm7
B♭7
E♭maj. 7
E♭6
got you under my skin. I
tried so not to give in, I
A♭m6
D
said to my-self,"This af-fair never will go so well." But
Dm7
G7
D♯dim.
C
why should I try to re-sist when, darling, I know so well I've
mf
marcato
p

A♭6
A♭m
B♭7
E♭maj. 7
E♭6
got you under my skin. I'd
Fm7
B♭7
E♭
E♭7
poco a poco cresc. ed appassionato
sac-ri-fice an-y-thing, Come what might, for the sake of hav-ing you near, In spite of a
poco a poco cresc. ed appassionato
A♭
A♭m
E♭
B♭7
molto cresc.
warn-ing voice that comes in the night And re-peats and re-peats in my ear: "Don't you
subito p
molto cresc.
Cm
f molto espressivo
A♭
B♭7
E♭
E♭dim.
know, lit-tle fool, you nev-er can win, Use your men-
f molto espressivo

Fm7
Bb7
Eb
Bb+
Eb
mf
-tal - i - ty,
Wake up to re - al - i - ty."
But each
mf
Ab
cresc.
Abm
Eb
p rit
Bbm
C7
Guitar tacet
time I do, just the thought of you makes me stop,
Be-fore I be - gin,
'Cause I've
cresc.
p rit
p dolce
Fm
a tempo
Bb7(9b)
Eb
1.
poco rit
got you under my skin.
I've
a tempo
rit
ppp a tempo
poco rit
2. Fm7
Bb7
Eb
Bb7
Eb
poco rall.
più rall.
R.H.
morendo
ppp
8

I ONLY HAVE EYES FOR YOU

Words by AL DUBIN
Music by HARRY WARREN

I don't know if we're in a garden, Or on a crowded av-e-
Dm7 G7 Em7 C Em C9 F Fm G7
-nue. You are here, so am I Maybe mil-lions of people go
Em7 C A♭7 G7 Fm Dm7/G Gm G7 Dm7
by, But they all dis-ap-pear from view, And I
Dm7 G G7 C Em C E7 (♭5) A7 A7(♭9)
1. 2.
on-ly have eyes for you. Are you you.
Dm7 Fm G7 C Dm7 C

ISLE OF CAPRI

Words by JIMMY KENNEDY
Music by WILHELM GROSZ

Fate chang'd it all And I'm left to re - call.
Lost love, it seems You just bring emp-ty dreams.
Fm B7 Db7 C Db7 C7
EFRAIN
'Twas on the Isle of Ca-pri that I found her Beneath the shade of an old wal-nut tree Oh! I can
mp-mf
F Gm7 C7
still see the flow'rs blooming round her Where we met on the Isle of Ca - pri. She was as
Gm7 C7 F C7 F
sweet as a rose at the dawn-ing But somehow fate had-n't meant her for me And tho' I
F Gm7 C7
sail'd with the tide in the morn-ing Still my heart's on the Isle of Ca - pri.
Gm7 C7 F C7 F

Summer time was near - ly ov - er Blue It - al - ian sky a - bove,
B♭ F C7 F
I said "La-dy I'm a rov - er, Can you spare a sweet word of love?" She whisper'd
B♭ F G7 C7
soft - ly "It's best not to lin - ger" And then as I kiss'd her hand I could see She wore a
F Gm7 C7
1 2
plain golden ring on her fin-ger 'Twas good-bye on the Isle of Ca - pri. 'Twas on the pri.—
Gm7 C7 F C7 F F C7 F
D. S. 𝄋

IN A SHANTY IN OLD SHANTY TOWN

Words by JOE YOUNG
Music by LITTLE JACK LITTLE and JOHN SIRAS

REFRAIN

It's on - ly a shan - ty in old Shan - ty Town,........... The
a tempo
p - mf
F A7 D7
roof is so slan - ty it touch - es the ground; But my
G7 F♯9 G9
tum - bled down shack, By an old rail - road track, Like a
C7 G7 C7 F B♭ D♭7 F D7
mil - lion - aire's man - sion, is call - ing me back............... I'd
G7 Dm7 B♭m G7 C7

give up a pal-ace if I were a king; It's more than a
F A7 D7 G7
pal-ace, it's my ev-'ry-thing. There's a queen wait-ing
ad lib.
colla voce
F♯9 G9 B♭ (dim) B♭
there with a sil-ver-y crown, In a shan-ty in
B♭m F A7 D7 Gm G7
old Shan-ty Town. It's Town.
a tempo
rit.
C7 F B♭ F B♭m Am C7 F
8
D.C.

IT'S A SIN TO TELL A LIE

Words and Mu
by BILLY MAYHE

tell a lie. Mil-lions of hearts have been bro -
E7 F A7 Dm G7 Cdim
-ken, Just be-cause these words were spo - ken. I love you, yes, I
C D7 Fm G7 C
do, I love you, If you break my heart I'll die.
G(5♯) C E7 F A7
So be sure it's true, when you say "I love you," It's a sin to
Dm F Fm C Gm A7 D7
1 2
tell a lie! Be sure it's lie!
G7 C dim G7 C F Fm C

I'VE TOLD EV'RY LITTLE STAR

Words by OSCAR HAMMERSTEIN
Music by JEROME KER

I can write po - ems, too, When you're far a - way,
C
G7
C
C°
When you're far a - way, I write po - ems too.
G7
G♯7
Am
F
G7
C
But when you are near, my lips go dry. When you are near
più espress.
C7
F
C7
F
Gm7
I on - ly sigh: Oh, dear.
(spoken)
poco deliberato e marcato
C7
Gm7
(C Bass)
C7
F

REFRAIN

p
I've told ev-'ry lit-tle star Just how sweet I think you are,
F C7 F C7
Why have-n't I told you? I've told
F C7 F C7 F
rip-ples in a brook, Made my heart an o-pen book, Why have-n't
C7 F C7 F C7 F
I told you?
Gm7 C7 F
Friends ask me: Am
mp
C

I in love? I al - ways an - swer "Yes," Might as well con -
G7
C
C6
C°
G7
- fess, If I don't, they guess. May - be
p
p
Am
F
G7
C
C9
F
you may know it too, Oh, my dar - ling, if you do, Why have - n't
Gm7
C7
F
F#°
Gm
Gmb5
F
you told me?
pp
C7
F
C7
F

THE LADY IS A TRAMP

Words by LORENZ HART
Music by RICHARD RODGERS

E9 E7 A7 D9 D7 G7 G+
las I missed the Beaux-Arts Ball and what is twice as sad, I was
C Am F G7 C G+ Gm Edim
nev - er at a par - ty where they hon - ored No - el Ca - 'ad. But
D7 Dm7 Em F Em Dm D7
so - cial cir - cles spin too fast for me, My
L.H.
G7 E♭ Dm7 Em B G7
Ho - bo - hem - ia is the place to be.

Refrain
p-mf
C
Cm7
Dm7
G7
I get too hun-gry For din-ner at eight,
p-mf
C
Cm7
Dm7
G7
I like the thea-tre but nev-er come late.
C
Cmaj7
C9
F
Fm6
I nev-er both-er with peo-ple I hate,
C
C+
F
G7
C
G7
That's why the la-dy is a tramp.
mf

C
Cm7
Dm7
G7
I don't like crap-games With Bar - ons and Earls,
Won't go to Har - lem In er - mine and pearls
Cmaj7
C9
F
Fm6
Won't dish the dirt with the rest of the girls,
C+
That's why the la - dy is a tramp.
I like the

Fmaj7
G7
Em7
Am
Dm7
free fresh wind in my hair, Life with-out care.
mf
G7
C
A7
D7
G7
C
Cm7
I'm broke, it's oke, Hate Cal-i-for-nia, It's
p
Dm
E7
Am
C+
Am7
1.
D7
G7
C
Am
Dm7
G7
cold and it's damp, That's why the la-dy is a tramp.
mf
2.
D7
D7♭5
G7
C
Em
Cm7
Dm
Fm
G7
C
la-dy is a tramp.
f
sf

I WON'T DANCE

Words by OSCAR HAMMERSTEIN II and OTTO HARBACH
Music by JEROME KERN

1 REFRAIN

p
I won't dance! Don't ask me; I won't dance! Don't ask me; I won't dance, Ma-dame, with
C Cmaj7 Dm G7 C Cmaj7 Dm G7 C Cmaj7 Dm G7
you. My heart won't let my feet do things they should do!
C Cmaj7 C7 C11 F Fm G7 C Dm G7
f
You know what? You're love-ly, (SHE) And so what? I'm love-ly! (HE) But oh! What you do to me!
C Cmaj7 Dm7 G7 C Cmaj7 Dm7 G7 C(9) C Cmaj7 Dm7 G7 C Cma
— I'm like an o-cean wave that's bumped on the shore; I feel so ab-so-lute-ly
C7 C11 F Fm G7 C G7 C Gm7 C7 F
stump'd on the floor! (SHE) When you dance you're charming and you're gen-tle!
mf
mp
Fm G7 C Dm7 G7 Ab Ab7

'Spec-ially when you do the "CON-TI-NEN-TAL."
(HE) But this feel-ing is-n't pure-ly
D♭ C D♭7 B B7
men-tal; For heav-en rest us, I'm not as-bes-tos. And that's why
C7 E7 Am Dm9 G7
p
I won't dance! Why should I? I won't dance! How could I? I won't dance! Mer-ci beau-
C Cmaj7 Dm7 G C Cmaj7 Dm7 G C Cmaj7 Dm7 G7
-coup! I know that mu-sic leads the way to ro-mance: So if I
cresc.
C C7 C11 F Fm G7 C C7 C11
hold you in my arms I WON'T DANCE!
mf
p
sf
Fmaj7 B♭6 A A♭7 G11 G7 C C♯° Dm7 A♭7 C

SMOKE GETS IN YOUR EYES

Words by OTTO HARBACH
Music by JEROME KERN

-side, Can-not be de-nied."
Fm7
B♭7
E♭
B♭7/E♭
They said "some-day you'll find, All who love are blind, When your heart's on
accel
E♭
B♭11
B♭7
E♭
E♭+
A♭
A0
a tempo
fire, You must re-a-lize Smoke gets in your eyes."
E♭maj7
E♭6
Fm7
B♭7
E♭
Un poco piu mosso
mf
So I chaffed them and I gai-ly laughed to think they could doubt my love.
B
Bmaj7
B
F♯7
F♯0
F♯7

8. E♭
Yet to - day My love has flown a - way, I am with -
B
A♭m7
B♭7
p
poco rit.
p a tempo
-out my love. Now laugh-ing friends de
p
poco rit.
p a tempo
E♭
B♭7/E♭
E♭
poco rit.
-ride Tears I can-not hide. So I smile and
poco rit.
B♭7
E♭
E♭+
A♭
A0
say, "When a love-ly flame dies, Smoke gets in your eyes."
3
allarg.
E♭maj7
E♭6
Fm7
B♭7
E♭

I'VE GOT THE WORLD ON A STRING

Words by TED KOEHLER
Music by HAROLD ARLEN

REFRAIN

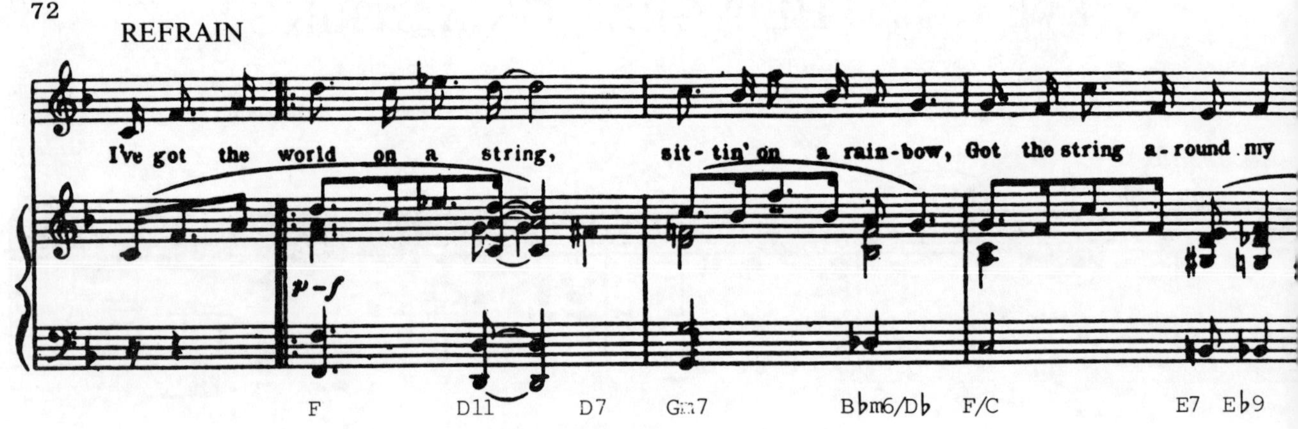
I've got the world on a string, sit-tin' on a rain-bow, Got the string a-round my
p-f
F D11 D7 Gm7 B♭m6/D♭ F/C E7 E♭9

.... - ger What a world what a......... life I'm in love! I've got
A♭m6 Gm7 C7 A♭° C7 C11 C13 F F+ C C7(♭5) C7

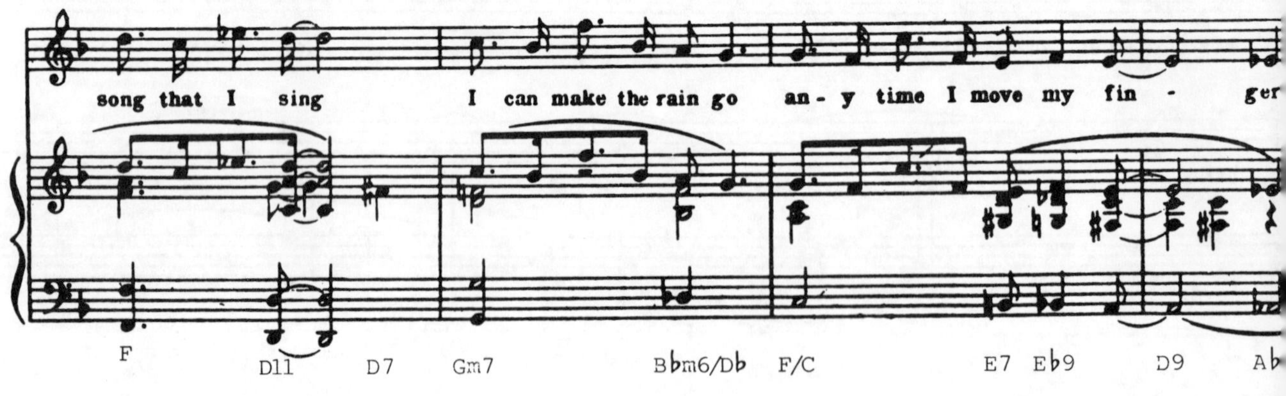
song that I sing I can make the rain go an-y time I move my fin - ger
F D11 D7 Gm7 B♭m6/D♭ F/C E7 E♭9 D9

Luck-y me can't you see I'm in love,................ Life is a beau-ti-ful thing,
Gm7 C7 A♭° C7 C11 C13 F F7 F° B♭m F A9

As long as I hold the string,..
I'd be a sil - ly so and so,
D9
G13
If I should ev - er let go,......................................
I've got the world on a string,
G7 (+5)
B♭
D♭9 (+5)
C13
F
D11
D7
sit - tin' on a rain - bow, Got the string a - round my fin - ger, What a world, what a
Gm7
B♭m6/D♭
F/C
G13
G7 (+5)
Gm7
.... life... I'm in love!................................. I've got the love!.................................
Bell
C13
F
D♭7
C13
F
F
D♭9
F

KEEP YOUNG AND BEAUTIFUL

Words by AL DU
Music by HARRY WARR

charm still re - mains.
After you grow
-tain it for boys,
Old age is - n't
Gm D7 Gm D7 Gm Fm B♭7
old, ba - by, You don't have to be a cold ba - by.
real, ba - by, You are as old as you feel ba - by.
poco rit.
E♭ Cm7 Fm7 F9 F9(♭5) B♭13 B♭7aug
REFRAIN
Keep young and beau - ti - ful,.... It's your du - ty to be
a tempo
E♭ Fm7 B♭7 E♭7 B♭7 E♭ Fm7 B♭7
beau - ti - ful,.... Keep young and beau - ti - ful,.... If you want to be
E♭ E♭7 A♭ D E♭ E♭7 C7 Fm7 B♭7

loved. Don't fail to do your stuff,... With a lit-tle powder
E♭ A♭ E♭ Fm7 E♭ Fm7 B♭7 E♭ E♭ Fm7 B♭7
and a puff,.... Keep young and beau-ti - ful,... If you want to be
E♭ E♭7 A♭ D7 E♭ C9 C7 Fm7 B♭7
loved.......... If you're wise, ex-er-cise all the fat off. Take it
E♭ A♭ E♭ E♭7 A♭ E♭7 A♭ E♭7
off, off-a here, off-a there............. When you're seen an-y-where with your
A♭ E♭7 Fm A♭aug A♭ F7 B♭ F7

hat off, Have a mar - cel wave in your hair,
Bb F7 Bb F7 Fm Db7 Bb7
Take care of all those charms,... And you'll al-ways be in
Eb Fm7 Bb7 Eb Bb7 Eb Fm7 Bb7
some - one's arms,... Keep young and beau - ti - ful,.....
Eb Ebmaj7 Eb7 Eb7 aug Ab D7 Eb Eb7 C9 C7
If you want to be loved................. loved................
Fm7 Bb7 Eb Ab Eb Bb13 Eb Ab Eb
1
2
f
sfz
D.C.

SOUTH OF THE BORDER

Words and Music by
JIMMY KENNEDY and MICHAEL CARR

pic - ture in old Span-ish lace Just for a ten - der while I
Eb Ab Bb7 Eb
kissed the smile up - on her face For it was "Fi - es - ta" and we were so
Eb° Bb7 Eb Eb7
gay South of the Bor - der down Mex - i - co way
Ab Eb Ab Bb7 Eb
Then she sighed as she whispered "Ma - ña - na" Nev-er dream-ing that we were parting And I
Eb Fm Bb7 Eb
lied as I whispered "Ma - ña - na" For our to - mor-row nev - er came South of the
Eb C7 Fm Abm Eb Bb7 Eb

Bor - der I rode back one day There in a veil of white by
E♭ A♭ B♭7 E♭
can - dle-light she knelt to pray The Miss-ion bells told me
E♭° B♭7 E♭
that I must - n't stay South of the Bor - der down Mex-i-co
E♭7 A♭ E♭ A♭ B♭7
way Ay! Ay! Ay! Ay! Ay! Ay! Ay! Ay!
E♭ B♭7 E♭
Ay! Ay! Ay! Ay! Ay! Ay! Ay! Ay!
p
rit.
B♭7 E♭ A♭m E♭

PICK YOURSELF UP

Words by DOROTHY FIELDS
Music by JEROME KERN

REFRAIN (Polka tempo)

mp
Will you remember the fa-mous men, Who had to fall to rise a-gain? So take a deep breath,
(He breathes audibly)
mp
Gm C7 Fmaj7 B♭maj9 Em7 A7-9 Dm7 G9 Gm7 C7 Gm7 C7
PICK YOURSELF UP,
(Business)
DUST YOURSELF OFF,
START ALL OVER A - GAIN.
Fine.
Gm7 C7 Gm7 C7 Gm7 C7 Gm7 C7 F
p
He. I'll get some self- as - sur-ance if your en - durance is great. I'll learn by
p leggiero
F Fmaj7 F6 F C7 F Fmaj7
eas - y stages if you're cour - a-geous and wait. To feel the strength I want to, I
F6 F C7 F Am Am(maj7) Am6 Am
poco a poco rall.
must hang on to your hand, May-be by the time I'm fif - ty I'll get up and do a nif - ty.
D.S.
Bm7 G7 Am Am7 Am6 Gm7 C7

SEPTEMBER IN THE RAIN

Words by AL DUBIN
Music by HARRY WARREN

an Au-tumn breeze, Back to my mem - o - ry.
will live al - ways, Un - til I end my days.
Fm
Bb7
Cm
F7
Ab
Bb7
Bb7
REFRAIN
The leaves of brown came tum-bling down, re - mem - ber? In Sep-
p-mf
Bb+
Eb
Gm
Cm
Gm
Fm
Ab
-tem - ber, In the rain, The sun went out just
Abm
Bb7
Eb
Bb+
Eb
Gm
like a dy - ing em - ber, That Sep-tem - ber, in the
Cm
Gm
Fm
Ab
Abm
Bb7

rain; To ev-ry word of love I heard you whis-per
Eb Ab Eb Bbm Eb7 Bbm Eb7 Ab
The rain-drops seem'd to play a sweet re-frain, Thou
poco rit.
Cm F7 Cm F7 Bb7 Fm Bb7 Fm Bb7 Bb7
Spring is here, to me it's still Sep-tem-ber, That Sep-tem-ber,
a tempo
Eb Gm Cm Gm Fm Ab Abm
1. 2.
in the rain. The rain
mf
pp
Bb7 Eb Ab Eb Bb+ Eb Ab Eb

LOVE LETTERS IN THE SAND

Words by NICK KENNY and CHAS KENNY
Music by J FRED COOTS

VERSE

REFRAIN

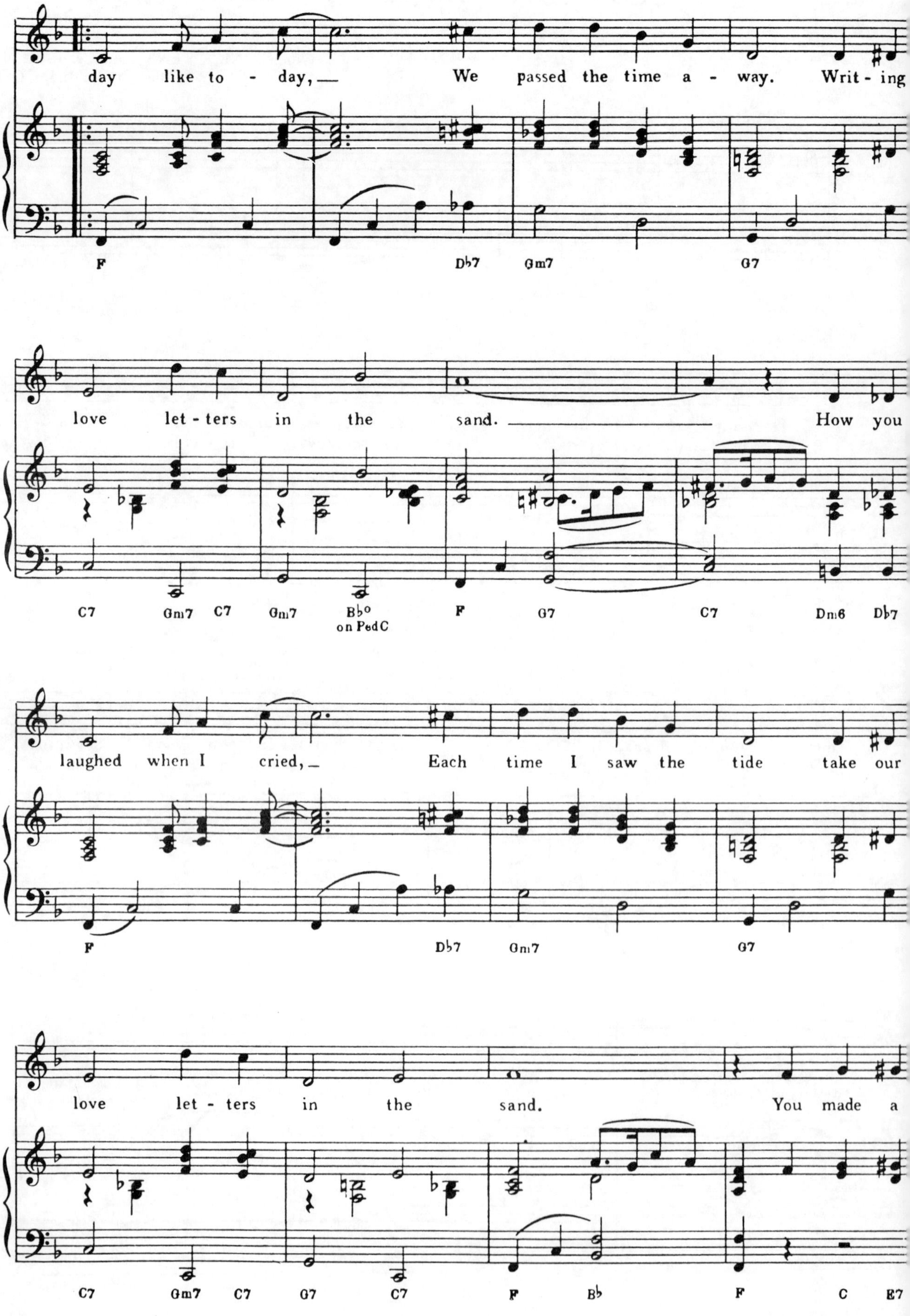
day like to - day, — We passed the time a - way. Writ - ing
F Db7 Gm7 G7
love let - ters in the sand. How you
C7 Gm7 C7 Gm7 Bb° on Ped C F G7 C7 Dm6 Db7
laughed when I cried, — Each time I saw the tide take our
F Db7 Gm7 G7
love let - ters in the sand. You made a
C7 Gm7 C7 G7 C7 F Bb F C E7

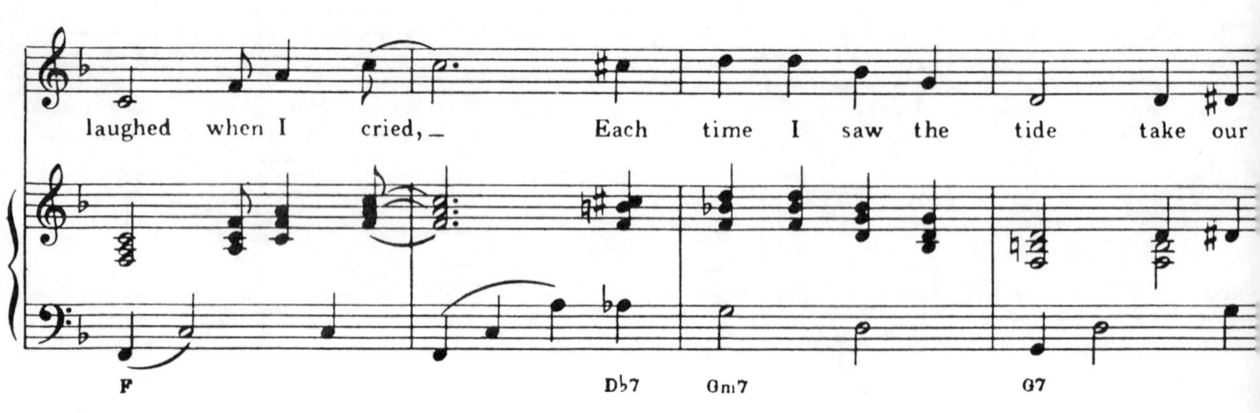

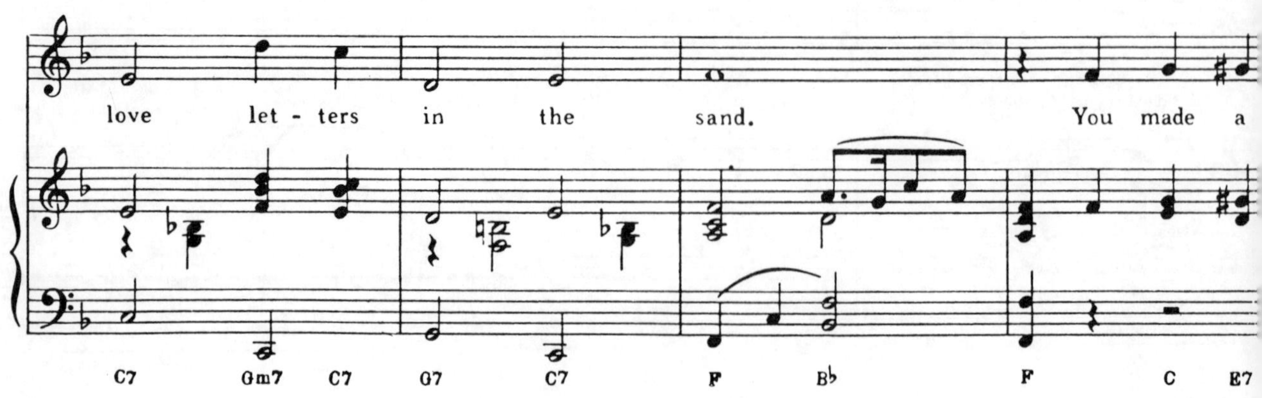

vow that you would al - ways be true, — But some - how that
A7 Gm7 Gm6 A7 Dm G7
vow meant noth - ing to you. — Now my poor heart just aches —
Dm7 G7 Gm C7 Dm6 D♭7 F
— With ev - 'ry wave that breaks ov - er Love let - ters
D♭7 Gm7 G7 C7 Gm7 C7
1. 2.
in the sand. On a sand. —
G7 C7 F G7 C7 Dm6 D♭7 F B♭ F

PARADISE

Words by NACIO HERB BROWN and GORDON CLI
Music by NACIO HERB B

grand, my love.
A+
A7/G
Dm6/F
A7/E
We lived and loved, our day is through, But each night in
Dm
E♭9
Dm
D♭7
G
dreams it's start - ed a - new, {He / She} comes to me as {he / she}
A♭9
G
E♭9
Dm
used to do my love!
Gm6
Dm
A7
F7

REFRAIN
And then {she / he} holds my hand, Mm Then Cu-
takes com-mand, Mm {Her / His} eyes re-
-veal a love that's real, And the sweet smile I
see Brings heav'n to me! And then {her / his} lips me-
mp-f
B♭
F7
B♭
F7
B♭7
E♭
E♭m
C7
F7
B♭

mine, Mm
With kiss-es so di-
F7
B♭
-vine, Mm
{Her His} love, each fond ca-ress, They lead the
F7
B♭
B♭+
way to hap-pi-ness, {She He} takes me to Par-a-
Opt.
rall.
a tempo
E♭
E♭m6/C
B♭
Cm
F7
1
2
-dise!
And then {she he}
-dise!
B♭
B♭+
Dm
F+
B♭

RED SAILS IN THE SUNSET

Words and Mus
JIMMY KENNEDY and HUGH WILLI

home safely to me
He sail'd at the dawning
all day I've been blue
D7
G
G
G7
C
Cmi
G
RED SAILS IN THE SUN-SET
I'm trusting in
you
Swift wings you must
G
D dim
C
D7
D7
G
G+
C
Cmi
bor-row
Make straight for the shore
We
mar-ry to-mor-row
G
D7
G
G+
C
Cmi
G
And he goes sailing no more
RED SAILS IN THE SUNSET
'Way out on the sea
A7
D7
C
D7
G
G7
C
Cmi
G
1
2
Oh, car-ry my lov'd one
home safely to me.
me.
G
Ddim
C
D7
D7
G
F9th
G
G7
C
Cmi
G
D. S.

SEPTEMBER SONG

Words by MAXWELL ANDERSO
Music by KURT WEI

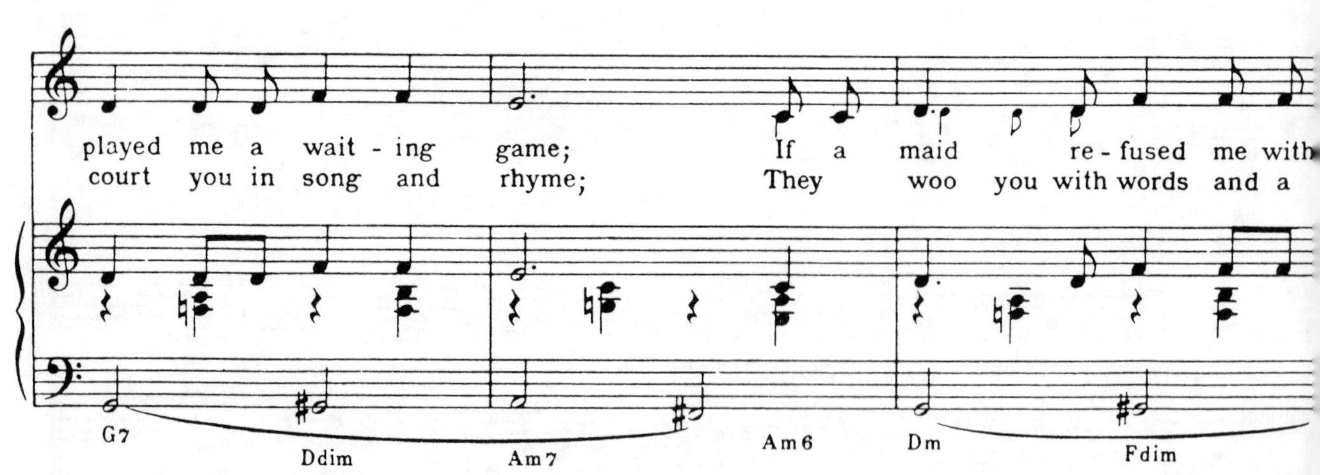

toss - ing curls I let the old earth take a coup-le of whirls While I
clo - ver ring, But if you ex - am - ine the goods they bring They have
Am7 Gdim Dm6 G+ C Am
plied her with tears in lieu of pearls. And as time came a - round she
lit - tle to of - fer but the songs they sing, And a plen - ti - ful waste of
Fm G7 Am Am6 Dm Fdim
came my way, As time came a - round she came.
time of day A plen - ti - ful waste of time.
Am Am6 Dm G7 C

REFRAIN (*with expression*)

For the days dwindle down to a pre - cious few
Sep-tem - ber, No - vem - ber, And these few
pre - cious days I'd spend with you, These gold-en days I'd
spend with you. When you you.
mp
poco espressivo
Fm
Cdim
più espress. e cresc.
mf
mp calmato
C
Cm
Ab
D7
poco rit.
a tempo
rit.
1
2

STAY AS SWEET AS YOU ARE

AIN
mp-mf
C F0 C F0 C B C Dm7 G7 Dm7 G7 C C0 Dm7 G7
Stay As Sweet As You Are, Don't let a thing ev-er change you. Stay As Sweet As You Are, Don't let a
C B C Bm7-5 E7 E+E7 Fmaj7 G13 Am Am7 D7
soul re-ar-range you. Don't ev-er lose all the charm you pos-sess, — Your love-li-ness,
Fm6 G7+ Dm7 G7 C F0 C F0 C B C Dm7 G7 Dm7 G7
— Dar-ling, the way you say "yes" — Stay As Sweet As You Are, Discreet as you are, you're di-vine, Dear.
C C0 Dm7 G7 C Bm7-5 E7 E+ E7 Fmaj7 Em Am
tay as grand as you are And as you are, tell me that you're mine, Dear. Young and gay or old and gray, Near to me or a-
D9 Fmaj7 F Fm(maj7) Fm6 C C0 G7 1 C G7+ 2 C
rall al fine
far, Night and day I pray That you'll always Stay As Sweet As You Are. Are.
L.H.

THERE'S A SMALL HOTEL

Words by LORENZ HA
Music by RICHARD RODGI

HE
Am7 F# G Am7 Bb+ Gmaj7 G6
A cer-tain place I know, Frank-ie, Where fun-ny peo-ple can have fun.
Am7 D7 B7 B7(b5) E7 rit. A7 D7 G7 Am7 rit. D7
That's where we two will go, Darl-ing, Be-fore you can count up One, Two Three. For:
rit
rit
REFRAIN
Gmaj7 G6 Gmaj7 G6 G
p
There's a small ho - tel With a wish - ing well; I
Am7 D7 Gmaj7 G6 Gmaj7 G6
wish that we were there to - geth - er.
mf
3

Gmaj7 G6 Gmaj7 G6 G G
p
There's a brid - al suite; One room bright and neat, Com -
Am7 D7 Gmaj7 G6 Gmaj7 G6
plete for us to share to - geth - er.
mf
C Dm7 G7 C D#dim Bm7 E7
Look - ing through the win - dow you can see a dis - tant stee - ple;
Am Bm7 E7 F Am Cm6 D7
Not a sign of peo - ple, Who wants peo - ple?

Gmaj7 G6 Gmaj7 G6 G
When the stee - ple bell says, "Good - night, sleep well," we'll
p
Am7 D7 Gmaj7 G6 Am7 D7
1.
thank the small ho - tel to - geth - er.
2.
Am7 D7 B♭ Cm7 F7
tel. We'll creep in - to our lit - tle shell And we will
G Am7 D7 Gmaj7 rit
thank the small ho - tel to - geth - er.
rit
L.H. mf

WALKIN' MY BABY BACK HOME

Words and Music by
ROY TURK and FRED E AHLERT

mead-ow and farm, — Walk-in' My Ba - by Back Home. We go 'long - har-mo-niz - in' a song, —
worn out my feet, — Walk-in' My Ba - by Back Home. Some girls fuss — if you don't take a 'bus —
E♭ B7 Fm7 B♭7 E♭
Or I'm re-cit - ing a poem. Owls go by, — and they give me the eye, — Walk-in' My Ba - by Back Home. — We
She doesn't care — if we roam, She don't strike — 'cos she knows that I like — Walk-in' My Ba - by Back Home. — What-
F9 B♭7 E♭
stop for a-while, She gives me a smile, And snuggles her head to my chest. — We start in to pet, — And that's when I get —
-ev-er I do — My ba-by does too, For she's that af - fec-tionate kind. — The cold wind may blow. — Her knees they may show, —
Gm C7 E♭/B♭ F7/A D7sus D7 Gm C7
Her pow-der all o-ver my vest. — Af-ter I — kind-a straighten my tie, — She has to bor-row my comb.
But some-how she don't seem to mind. When it rains, well, she nev - er com-plains, She's got a pain in her dome. But
F7 B♭7 E♭ F9
One kiss, then — I con-tin - ue a - gain, — Walk-in' My Ba - by Back Home.
I get 'flu — 'cos I'm al-ways wet through Walk-in' My Ba - by Back Home.
1 2
B♭7 E♭ B7 Fm B♭7 E♭

THE WAY YOU LOOK TONIGHT

Words by DOROTHY FIELDS
Music by JEROME KERN

A♭ Fm7 E♭6 B♭7 E♭ E♭6 a tempo Fm B♭ E♭ E♭6
And the way you look to - night.
a tempo
Fm B♭7 E♭ Cm Fm7 B♭7
Oh, but you're love - ly, With your smile so warm
E♭ C7♭9 Fm7 B♭7 rall. E♭7
And your cheek so soft, There is noth-ing for me but to love
3
rall.
A♭ Fm7 E♭6 B♭7 E♭ E♭6 a tempo Fm B♭
you, Just the way you look to - night.
a tempo

Eb Eb6 Fm Bb7 Gb mp cantabile Bbm6 Abm
With each word your ten-der-ness grows,—
mp cantabile
Db7 Gb Bbm Gbdim Db9
— Tear-ing my fear a - part,
mp Gb Gbdim Abm7 Db7(6) Gb maj.7 Gb
And that laugh that wrink-les your nose Touch-es my
mp
Ebm Bb7(Eb) Bb7 p Eb Cm
fool - ish heart. Love - ly,
p

Fm7 B♭7 E♭7 C7 Fm7
nev - er, nev - er change, Keep that breath-less charm, Won't you please ar -
B♭7 rall. E♭7 A♭ Fm7
range it, 'Cause I love you, Just the way you
rall.
E♭6 B♭7 E♭ E♭6 (bouche fermée) Fm7 B♭7 E♭maj.7 E♭6
look to - night, mm — mm — mm —
A♭maj.7 B♭ A♭6 G B♭dim Fm E♭6 B♭7 E♭ rall.
mm — Just the way you look to - night.
rall.
pp
Ped. *

WHAT A DIFF'RENCE A DAY MADE

Music and Spanish Words by MARIA GREVER
English Words by STANLEY ADAMS

Dmi F G7 F G7 C7
you dear, My lone-ly nights are thru dear, Since you said you were mine,
car - te, Que el be - so que ne - gas - te. Ya no lo pue-des dar,
Bb C7 F
What a diff-'rence a day makes, There's a rain-bow be-fore me, Skies a-bove can't be
Cuan-do vuel-va a tu la - do, Y es - té so - la con-ti - go. Las co-sas que te
Bb C7 F7
storm - y Since that mo-ment of bliss; That thrill-ing kiss. It's heav-en
di - go, No re - pi - tas ja - más, Por com - pa - sión. U - ne tu la-bio al
Bb F dim. Bb
when you, Find ro-mance on your men - u. What a diff-'rence a day made,
mi - o, Y es - tre-cha-me en tus bra - zos. Y cuen-ta los la - ti - dos,
C7 1. F Bb C7 2. F Db7 F
And the diff-'rence is you. What a diff-'rence a you
De nues-tro co - ra - zón. Cuan-do vuel va a tu zón
L H.

WHERE OR WHEN

Words by LORENZ HAR
Music by RICHARD RODGER

Moderato

VERSE

slowly

Cm7 F7 Cm7 F7 Bb7 Eb7 Bb7 Eb7 Ab

When you're a-wake The things you think come from the dreams you dream. Thought has wings, —

p

Fm7 Abm6 Ab6 Bb7 Eb Cm7 F7

— And lots of things — are sel-dom what they seem. Some-times you think you've

Cm7 F7 B♭7 E♭7 B♭7 E♭7 A♭ Fm7
lived be-fore All that you live to - day. Things you do come back to you,
A♭m6 Fm7 B♭7 E♭ Fm B♭7 poco rit.
As though they knew the way. Oh, the tricks your mind can play!
poco rit.
REFRAIN (with tender expression)
E♭
a tempo
E♭6 E♭maj.7
It seems we stood and talked like this be - fore. We
a tempo
p
Fm7
looked at each oth-er in the same way then, But I can't re-mem-ber where or

E♭maj.7 E♭6 A♭m6 B°7 E♭ E♭6

when. The clothes you're wear - ing are the

E♭maj.7 Fm7

clothes you wore. The smile you are smil - ing you were smil - ing then,

E°maj.7 E♭6 Fm6 G7

But I can't re - mem - ber where or when.

Cm Fm7 G7(sus.4) G7 F G7 Cm

Some things that hap - pen for the first time, Seem to be

mp

Fm7 F7(sus.4) F7 Fm7 B♭7 E♭
hap - pen - ing a - gain. And so it
p
E♭6 E♭maj.7 E♭+ poco Fm a poco
seems that we have met be - fore, and laughed be -
poco a poco
Gm crescendo Fm e più Gm espressivo Fm(sus.4) Fm Gm B♭7
fore, and loved be - fore, But who knows where or
crescendo e più espressivo
1 E♭ Fm7 E♭maj.7 Fm7 B♭7 2. E♭ A♭m C♭ E♭
mf rit.
when! when!
mf mf rit L.H.

YOU MUST HAVE BEEN A BEAUTIFUL BABY

Words by JOHNNY ME
Music by HARRY WA

You must have been a beau-ti-ful ba - by, You must have been a won-der-ful child, When
p-mf (with a lilt)
G7 C Dm7 CO C C+ C7 F9 Cm7 F9 Cm7 A♭m F9
you were on-ly start-in' to go to kin-der-gar-ten, I bet you drove the lit-tle boys wild, And
A♭ B♭9 A♭ B♭7 E♭ CO Fm7 B♭7 G7
when it came to win-ning blue rib - bons, You must have shown the oth-er kids how, I can
C Dm7 CO C C+ C7 F9 Cm7 F9 Cm7 A♭m F7
see the judg-es eyes as they hand-ed you the prize, I bet you made the cu-test bow Oh! you
E♭ E♭+ Cm E♭+ E♭ Cm7 F9 CO
1
2
must have been a beau-ti-ful ba - by, Cause ba-by look at you now. You
E♭ G7 C7 C+ C7 F9 A♭ B♭7 E♭ G7 E♭
D.C.

YOUNG AND HEALTHY

Words by AL D
Music by HARRY WA

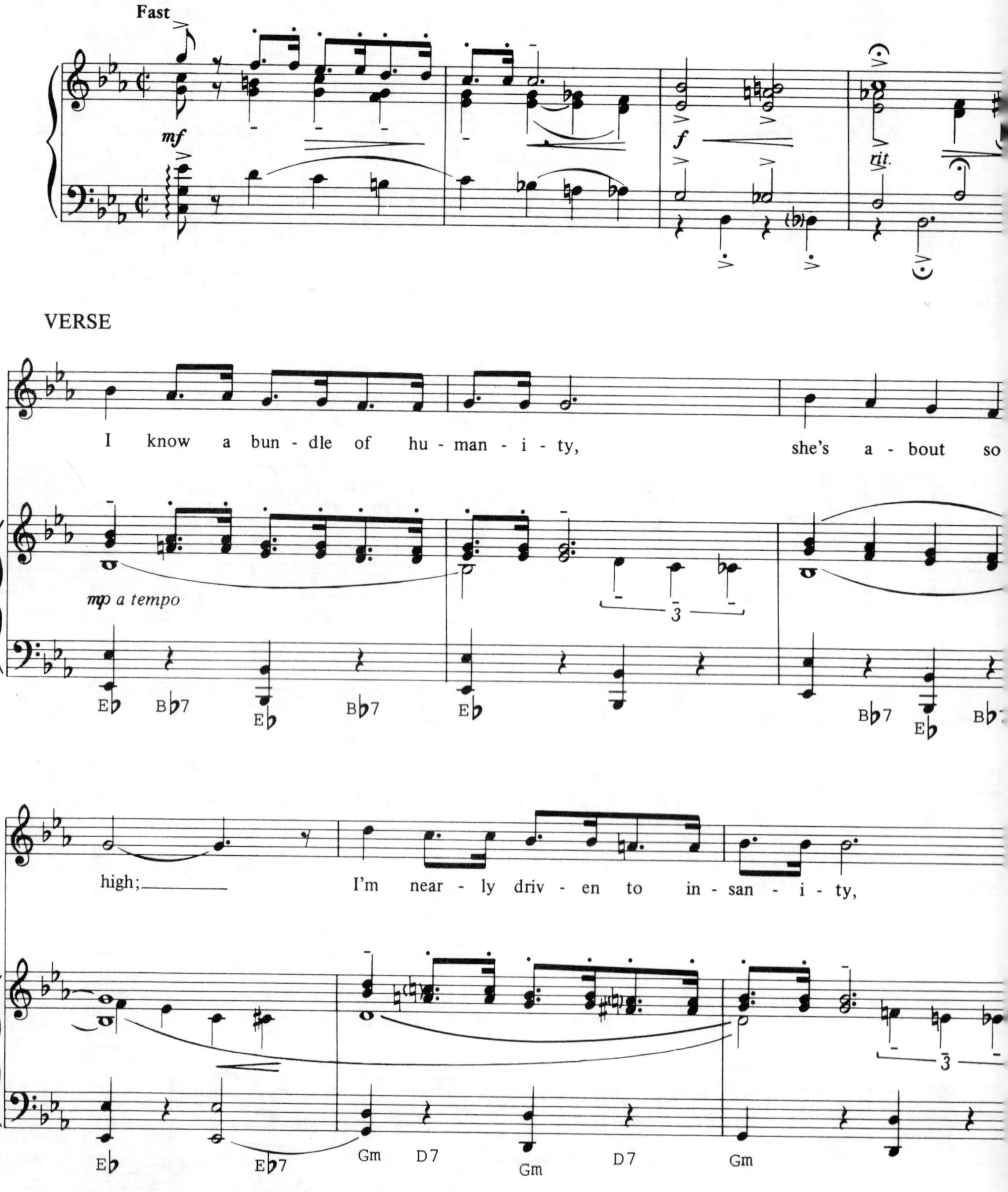

Fast
mf
f
rit.
VERSE
I know a bun - dle of hu - man - i - ty, she's a - bout so
mp a tempo
3
Eb Bb7 Eb Bb7 Eb Bb7 Eb Bb7
high; I'm near - ly driv - en to in - san - i - ty,
3
Eb Eb7 Gm D7 Gm D7 Gm

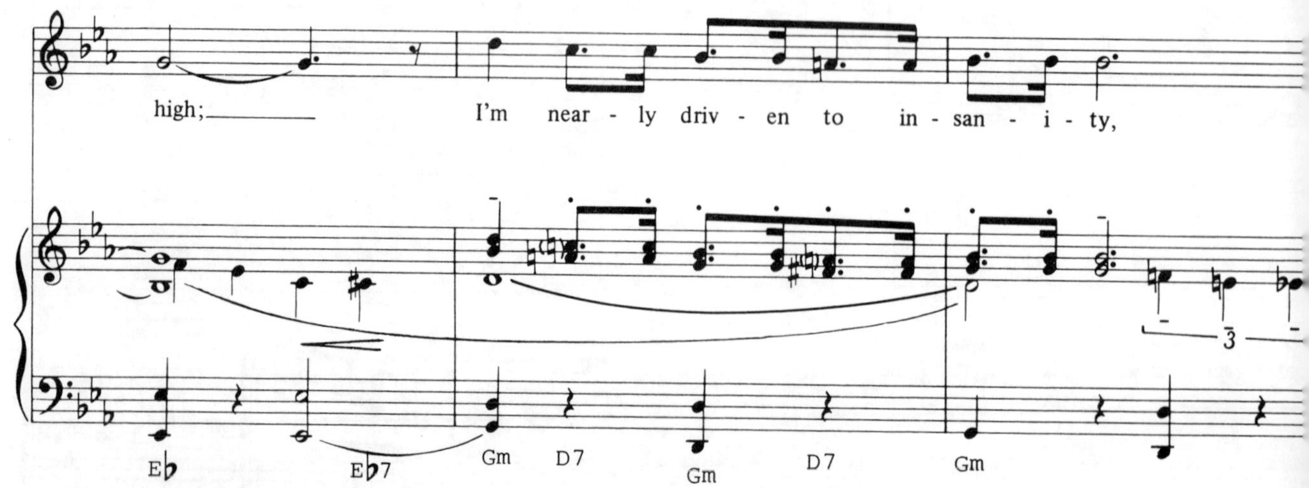

when she pass - es by. She's a snoot - y lit - tle cut - ie, she's
D7 Gm D7 Gm Cm7 Gm C7 Fm7 B♭7 E♭
mf
been so hard to kiss; I'll try to o - ver - come her
Fm7 Gm E♭ Fm7 B♭+5 E♭ B♭7 E♭ B♭7
rit.
van - i - ty, and then I'll tell her this:
E♭ Cm7 F7 B♭7
REFRAIN
p - f a tempo
I'm young and health - y, and you've got charms;
E♭ Fm7 B♭7 E♭ B♭7

it would real - ly be a sin not to have you in my
E♭ A⁰ B♭7 C7 F7 B♭7
arms. I'm young and health - y, and so a
E♭ B♭7 E♭ Fm7 B♭7 E♭
you; when the moon is in the sky, tell me, what
B♭7 E♭ A° B♭7 C7
I to do? If I could hate "yuh,"
F7 Gm E♭ Am7-5 D7 G Am7 D7

Printed in Great Britain by
St Edmundsbury Press Ltd, Bury St Edmunds, Suffolk